Printed and Published by D.C. Thomson & Co., Ltd.,
Dundee and London.
© D. C. Thomson & Co., Ltd., 1999
ISBN 0-85116-704-7

Hello, everyone!
Welcome to another brilliant
Twinkle Book — 64 colourful,
fun-packed pages specially for you!
Look out for super stories — The teddy who
couldn't squeak, Fenella and The dragon's
new toothbrush as well as Twinkle
favourites, Nurse Nancy, Silly Milly and
the Blobs.
You'll find great games,
puzzles and things to make and do, too —
all in the brightest book around.
Have fun!
Love,

Twinkle

The Blobs

Piggy Pink
wants to sing

It was a perfect day in Paintbox Land. The sun was shining, the bees were buzzing and the flowers were blooming.

Piggy Pink was so happy, she wanted to . . . *sing!*

At least, that's what she *would* have done, if she'd known how.

"Canary Yellow can sing," thought Piggy. "Maybe you have to *swing* to sing."

Piggy jumped on to a garden swing. She swung to and fro, trying to sing at the same time. But the only noise she made was a loud squeal when she fell off the swing and bumped her curly tail.

2–Piggy Pink walked on, until she arrived outside the Paintbox Land Nursery. One of the Blobs children was playing in the garden with a singing top.

"Hm! Maybe you have to *spin* to sing," thought Piggy.

So that's just what she did!

Round and round, faster and faster, spun the little piggy Blob.

"I can't sing like this," thought Piggy, getting dizzier and dizzier.

And the only noise she made this time was, "Ooh! I don't feel very well!"

3–Piggy set off home to Farmer Blob's farm. There she met the Cockerel, who agreed to teach Piggy to sing.

"Right, Piggy, after me," crowed the Cockerel. "One, two, three . . ."

"Cock-a-gruntle-doo!" grunted Piggy.

She tried again!

"Grunt-a-cockle-doo!"

4–And again!

"Snort-a-doodle-squeak!"

But it was hopeless. The Cockerel spent so long trying to teach Piggy Pink to sing, he lost his voice!

"Oh, dear," sighed Piggy. "Who will waken the Blobs tomorrow? I must practise all night until I get this right."

5–Next morning, the Blobs were up bright and early.

Who had wakened them? Not the Cockerel — he still had no voice.

Piggy Pink had wakened them.

Not by singing "Cock-a-doodle-doo", however, but by falling asleep and snoring like a pig.

Perhaps Piggy will learn to sing another day.

Nurse Nancy

1 — Nurse Nancy was the nurse at the Dollies Hospital. Early one morning, Nurse Nancy was woken up by the cry of 'Happy Birthday'. "Open *my* present first!" chuckled her brother.

4 — When Nancy returned to the hospital, she got a surprise! "Where *is* everyone?" she puzzled. "The waiting room's empty now!"

2 — Nancy loved her presents but, soon it was time to go to the hospital. "The waiting room is very crowded," Nancy thought.

3 — Then Mr Jingle, the doctor, appeared with a shopping list for Nancy. "Could you fetch these things, please?" he asked.

5 — Then Nancy went into the ward. Everyone was there! "Your grandad sent you out so we could prepare," Gemma chuckled.

6 — Nancy *was* happy! "What a lovely way to celebrate my birthday," she smiled. "A party with all my friends. Thank you!"

Dandy Lion

ONE winter morning, Dandy woke,
And shouted out, "Hooray!
The snow has fallen in the night.
I must go out to play!"

2 — Well, first of all he thought he'd make
A snowman, big and fat.
(It looks like Mrs Hippo and
He had to laugh at that!)

5 — There, lonely on a snowy branch,
Poor Mrs Cuckoo sat.
"*Cuckoo*! I hate the snow!" she shivered,
Under her woolly hat.

6 — Kind Dandy Lion put out his paw.
"Now, hop on here," said he.
"I think I know just what to do,
So come on home with me."

3 — Then, suddenly, he cried, "*Aha!*
   Some bird tracks in the snow!
I think that I will follow them,
   And find out where they go."

4 — Along the forest track he went,
   His nose close to the ground.
The marks came to an end and then
   He heard a little sound.

7 — He fetched his clock and made a small
   And cosy room inside!
"*Cuckoo*! I'll just *love* living here!"
   The happy birdie cried.

8 — Now every dawn at six o'clock,
   "*Cuckoo*! *Cuckoo*!" calls she.
Then Dandy jumps from bed to make
   Them both a cup of tea.

Pop-up Christmas Tree

THIS super pop-up Christmas tree is easy to make and you can decorate it, too.

Stick the following page to thin card and carefully cut round the top of the tree following the dotted black lines.

Fold along the black line so that the top of the tree pops up above the card.

Now you can have fun cutting out the Christmas ornaments and sticking them on your tree.

The teddy who couldn't squeak

TED BEAR was small and cuddly with soft, brown fur. But the special thing about Ted was that, if you pressed his tummy, he made a lovely, loud squeak.

One day, he was bought by Janey.

"I don't suppose any of her other toys will be able to squeak like me," chuckled Ted.

Then to Ted's astonishment, *all* Janey's toys squeaked when she introduced them.

"We *all* squeak," Patsy Panda said.

Poor Ted didn't feel special any more. Then he decided that he would be louder and better than the others!

He was so busy pressing his tummy that he didn't notice Janey's puppy bounce into the room. The puppy snatched up Ted playfully and rushed into the garden, where he eventually put Ted down by the hedge.

2 — Ted waited for Janey to come out to find him. But soon, he fell asleep and, a long time later, he was wakened by something tickling his nose.

"Goodness, it's morning and there are raindrops dripping on to my nose," gasped the little bear. "I've been here all night!"

Ted looked at his damp, brown fur and he pressed his tummy to squeak.

"The dampness has stopped my squeak!" gasped Ted.

3 — At breakfast-time, Ted heard Janey searching for him, but he couldn't squeak to give a clue to where he was. At last, she found him and scolded her puppy for taking Ted outside. That made Ted feel better and he was soon happy and dry again, inside the house. Later, Janey pressed the bear's tummy, but his squeak still didn't work.

"Oh, dear," she sighed. "You're ruined!"

"Oh, no!" Ted panicked. "Janey will never play with me again!"

4 — That night, Janey looked in the toy cupboard.

"I know which toy is going to be best for cuddling," she chuckled.

"Well, it won't be *me*," thought Ted, feeling very sorry for himself.

But, to his amazement, Janey lifted him off the shelf.

"You're the one because you won't make a noise," she laughed. "All the others squeak and keep waking me up."

And so, Ted became Janey's special bed-time bear.

"I don't care if I never squeak again," smiled the contented, little bear as he snuggled down under the cosy covers.

Silly Milly

She's always in a muddle

2 — Milly poured the mixture into a cake tin and Mum popped it into the oven. Milly was delighted to see, later, that her cake had turned out perfectly.

1 — One day, Milly was helping Mum arrange a surprise birthday party for Dad. Milly worked in the kitchen mixing the ingredients for his birthday cake.

4 — When the table had been laid with all the birthday food, Milly hung up the birthday banner. "That's as high as I can reach," she puffed.

5 — Mum had phoned some friends earlier, so all the guests arrived with plenty of time to spare. "Come in," Milly greeted them excitedly.

3 — Next, Milly helped Mum prepare other tasty goodies for the party. Then she set them out carefully on the table.

6 — Milly waited eagerly behind the curtains and, when Dad arrived, she asked everyone to be quiet. Then she switched off the light.

7 — But in the darkness, Milly slipped, knocking over the table and spilling the food over the guests. "Surprise!" she called. "Oh, yes, Milly," groaned Dad. "It *certainly* is!"

Snow-time puzzles

Jenny and her chums are playing with snowballs. Join in the fun by colouring the picture with your paints.

Help Sammy Snowman through the maze to reach his chum.

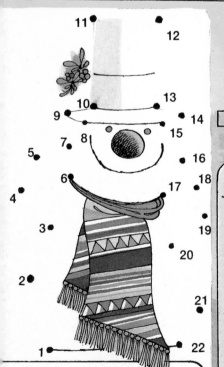

Join the dots to see someone with a jolly smile on his face.

Can you spot which two skaters are exactly alike?

Find six differences between these two pictures.

Twinkle

Willow Wood

1 — Lots of animals live in Willow Wood. One day, Spike, the hedgehog, found his friend Humbug, the badger, sitting by the river. "My, you look miserable!" he cried.

2 — "I'm fed up. I'd like to go rowing but I get seasick!" replied the sad badger. "And whoever heard of a badger being seasick? I feel so silly. What can I do?"

3 — "Barney will know," cried Spike, rushing off very quickly.

4 — The wise owl was in his workshop. "*Don't* disturb me! I'm busy!" he hooted. "That's not like Barney," thought Spike in surprise.

5 — Later, the little hedgehog was even *more* surprised when he met Humbug and the badger told him, "I'm puffed out. I've been doing lots of rowing!"

6 — "But-but-" spluttered Spike. "You told me . . ." "I know I said I get seasick," laughed Humbug, "but come and see what I've been given! It's fantastic!"

7 — "This is what Barney Owl was making," explained the badger. "It's a rowing machine. I can row on dry land and not feel seasick! It's just perfect for me!"

fun to colour

Piggy Pink

SWEETS

Fenella

FENELLA was a little Falabella horse.

Falabellas are the tiniest horses in the world.

Fenella lived with her family in the zoo's Children's Corner.

One day, the blacksmith came to give Claude the Clydesdale carthorse new shoes!

"Will I get shoes today?" Fenella asked her mummy.

"No, dear," her mum replied.

2 — Fenella was disappointed.

Next morning, Fenella pranced round to Claude's stable.

"Claude," she smiled, "could I try on your shoes?"

Claude burst into horsey laughter.

"Even if I *could* get them off, they'd be far too big for you, Fenella!" he chuckled.

Fenella examined Claude's hoofs, and had to agree.

3 — "Well," she sighed to herself, "I'll have to think of something."

Before settling down that night, Fenella noticed that the zoo keeper had left his rubber boots outside his front door, on the mat.

"Aha!" smiled Fenella. "Even if I can't have four shoes, two would be fine."

Gathering all her strength, the little horse leapt over the fence to her enclosure.

Very quietly, she slipped her front legs into the boots.

With a lot of difficulty, she scrambled back over her enclosure fence and fell asleep — still wearing the rubber boots!

The next morning, the other animals couldn't believe their eyes!

4 — There stood Fenella with her front legs in a *huge* pair of rubber boots!

"So *that's* where my boots went to!" smiled the zoo keeper, when he saw Fenella. "I really would like them back, if you don't mind. You don't need shoes. You don't go on hard roads, like Claude."

Fenella didn't mind at all. The boots were terribly heavy and far more uncomfortable than she'd imagined.

"The problem was that they were *boots* — not shoes," sighed Fenella. "A nice set of shoes would have been fine! I know I stay on the soft grass all the time, but I'd still love some shoes like Claude's. It really isn't fair."

5 — All week, Fenella was miserable.

Everyone felt very sorry for her — but they didn't know what to do.

The next Saturday was a very happy day at the zoo.

Mrs Gorilla had a new baby.

Presents arrived from visitors and friends — and soon the zoo keeper's house was full of rattles, dummies, knitted jackets, hats and mittens.

"Well," exclaimed the zoo keeper to his wife. "The baby gorilla won't need half of this stuff. We can give it to the hospital. But I know *exactly* what to do with *these*!"

6 — And, picking up a small parcel, he set off for the Children's Corner.

"Here you are, Fenella," he smiled. And he fastened four little baby booties around her hoofs. They fitted perfectly! And they weren't uncomfortable!

Fenella was delighted, and began to dance all around her enclosure to show off her new shoes!

"By the time you've worn those out," smiled the zoo keeper. "You'll hopefully, have gone off the idea of wearing shoes. But, if not, my wife could knit you more! It's lovely to see you happy again, Fenella!"

Toy-time fun!

To play this game, paste these two pages to card, then cut out all the toy pictures. Mix up the cards and place them face down on a table.

The first player starts by turning over two cards. If they match, the player keeps them and tries again, continuing until two cards are turned over that aren't a pair. Then the next player takes a turn.

The secret of the game is to remember where all the matching cards are. The winner is the player with the most pairs.

Patch

1 — Paula Perkins has a cute kitten called Patch. One day, Paula was decorating the tree.

2 — "Be careful, Patch. You have to put the tinsel on the Christmas tree, not on yourself," Paula chuckled.

3 — Next, the kitten chased a bright bauble — and burst it! "You naughty puss!" Paula scolded.

4 — But the playful puss couldn't stay still. He found some wrapping paper and rolled and rolled in it, loving the rustling sound.

5 — Soon, Paula was finished. "What do you think, Patch? Isn't the tree lovely?" she asked. But Patch was nowhere to be seen. "Patch!" called Paula. "Patch! Where are you?"

6 — Just then, a funny-shaped Christmas parcel rolled over the floor to Paula. "Oh, Patch!" she chuckled when she saw him inside. "You're the cutest present ever!"

Puzzle-time in SPACE

Spot six differences between these funny pictures of friendly space folk.

Join the dots to see what this is.

There are six pencils hidden on this page. Can you find them?

Help the spaceboy through the maze to reach his home planet.

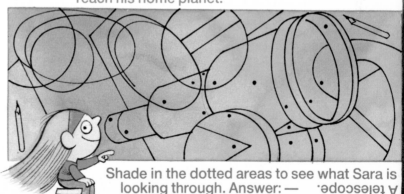

Shade in the dotted areas to see what Sara is looking through. Answer: — A telescope.

Which two of these stars are alike?

The Blobs

... bright little blobs of paint who come out of a paintbox into the wonderful world of Paintbox Land.

Grumbly Green and the weather

"Oh, dear! It's been snowing!" grumbled Grumbly Green one day. "I'll have to put on lots of cosy clothes before I go out."

So, Grumbly put on a jacket, woolly hat and scarf, a pair of warm mitts and his bright red boots. He carried his skis.

Then Grumbly looked out of the window. What a surprise he got! The sun was shining, the trees were green and some Blobs were actually sun-bathing!

"Goodness me!" he cried. "There's been a sudden change in the weather. *I'll* have to change, too!"

And so, Grumbly put away his skis and his boots and went in search of some cool clothes.

This time, Grumbly put on his shorts, sandals and sunglasses and he carried a deck-chair instead of skis.

"I suppose I'd better go out and enjoy myself," he said grumblingly.

But, oh, dear! What a shock he got when he stepped outside. Instead of a warm, sunny day, it was cold and snowy!

"Isn't it rather chilly for shorts?" asked Inky Black.

"Are those the latest thing in snowshoes?" laughed Poppy Red.

How *did* the weather change so suddenly? Rainbow Blob had put a picture of a sunny scene in front of Grumbly's window as a joke!

However, Grumbly was not amused!

"Huh! What a silly joke!" he muttered huffily in his grumbliest voice.

Mary Mouse steps out

ALL the mice at the Mouse Dancing School were excited. The mice were to give a concert and Queen Mouse was to choose the best dancer.

The mice decided to dress up as fairies and do a fairy dance and their mummies agreed to make the fairy costumes. But Mary Mouse's mummy could only find some red and white striped material in her sewing basket — not suitable for a fairy.

"I could make you a clown's outfit, Mary," she said. "Something different."

"But everyone else is doing a *fairy* dance!" Mary said.

Mary cheered up when Mrs Cheese, the teacher, found her some lively music.

2 — At the dress rehearsal for the concert, Mary thought the other mice looked very pretty in their fairy dresses. But they just laughed at Mary's costume.

"You *do* look odd," Mildred Mouse told her. "Why can't you be a fairy like us?"

3 — Soon, it was the day of the queen's visit. When the queen arrived in her carriage, Mrs Cheese led her to a special seat in the front row.

Then the concert began. Mrs Cheese played the piano as each of the mice came on stage and did her fairy dance with the others gradually joining in. Queen Mouse thought that the mice looked very sweet and they danced so prettily to the soft music. But every dance was the same — and soon the queen grew very sleepy. In fact, she was struggling to stay *awake!*

Just then, however, a drum roll made the queen sit up and take notice of Mary coming on stage. The little clown mouse twirled round and round, faster and faster. The queen clapped very loudly and Mary started to enjoy herself.

When the dance finally ended, Mary curtsied as the audience clapped and cheered. Then the other mice came on stage, because it was time for the queen to announce the winner.

4 — "I enjoyed the clown dance best. So the winner is — *Mary Mouse*!" said the queen.

Mary just couldn't believe it! Then the queen presented her with a gold trophy.

And, as Mary stood in front of the cheering audience, she thought that Mummy was right. Sometimes it *was* best to be different from everybody else!

Polly

1 — Polly Penguin lives in Snowland with her chums. One day, Polly, Peter Polar Bear and Rodney Reindeer were playing outside.

2 — Polly, Peter and Rodney decided to build a snowman. When they had finished, they stepped back to admire him.

4 — Sure enough, the snowman kept wobbling, until, at last, he toppled over and rolled right down to the bottom of the hill.

5 — The chums were fed up. "I'm *bored*," moaned Peter Polar Bear, "but I don't want to make another snowman."

3 — Just then, however, the big snowman began to wobble. "Look out! I think he's going to fall," cried Polly.

6 — The three friends tried hard to think of something to do. Then Polly had an idea. "*I know how we can have some fun!*" she cried.

7 — Soon, Polly, Peter and Rodney were whizzing down the track made by their falling snowman. "This *super* slide is fantastic!" they cried.

Old Macdonald's
Farmyard fun-time

Use the first letters of each of these objects to make a word. Answer: — Farm.

Join the dots to see which farmyard animal this is. Answer: — A cockerel.

Find six differences between these two pictures of Spot the sheepdog.

Unscramble these letters to help Jenny find out where her pony is. Answer: — STABLE.

Fill in the dotted areas to see Billy.

Which two of these ducks are exactly alike?

My Baby Brother

ONE morning when we woke, it was
As cold as it could be.
"You'll need your *winter* clothes today,"
Mum said to Ben and me.

2 — We put our nice thick jerseys on,
And to the kitchen flew.
"I've made hot porridge," Mummy smiled.
"You'll soon be warm right through!"

3 — Then, as we ate, we heard *tap-tap*!
Ben called, "Just look who's here!"
It's our friend Mister Robin,
Who used to come last year!"

4 — We scattered lots of crumbs for him,
Outside the window pane.
"The colour of *his* front and *mine*,"
Ben grinned, "Are just the same!"

5 — That afternoon we watched the leaves
   All blown about the sky.
"It's sad when summer days have gone,"
   Said Benny with a sigh.

6 — "Cheer up!" I said. "We'll have some fun.
   I've got a plan, you see!
Put on your jacket and your boots,
   And come outside with me."

7 — Then, with a broom, we swept the leaves
   Into a great big pile.
"That really is a help, you two!"
   Called Daddy with a smile.

8 — So hand in hand, we danced around
   Those leaves of brown and red.
"Great! Mister Robin's joining in!"
   My happy brother said.

The Blobs

... bright little blobs of paint who come out of a paintbox into the wonderful world of Paintbox Land.

Royal Blue
and the
cowboy

KING ROYAL BLUE had a guest staying at the palace. He was Bronco Blob from America. "I ride Broncos — wild horses — in rodeos at home," Bronco Blob told the king. "That's how I got my name."

Princess Powder Blue took Bronco sight-seeing. She showed the cowboy all round Paintbox Land and introduced him to her Blob chums.

After a while, though, Bronco seemed rather sad and asked to return to the palace.

Later, Royal Blue found Bronco in tears. The cowboy was upset because he felt very homesick.

"I don't mean to be ungrateful," sighed Bronco, "but I wish I had a rodeo horse to ride."

Royal Blue had an idea.

"Come with me, Bronco!" he cried. Royal Blue took Bronco to the fair.

Then he pointed to the carousel.

"*Yahoo!*" cried Bronco as the carousel ride began. "This is *almost* as much fun as the rodeo!"

Sara and Sam

1 — Sara and Sam Bright were building a snowman in their garden when Grandad arrived. "Hi, kids!" called Grandad. "That's a fine looking snowman you've made."

2 — The children were *thrilled* when they discovered that Grandad had made a super sledge, specially for them. "It's *brill*, Grandad!" cried Sam. "I can't *wait* to try it."

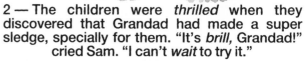

3 — Mum was too busy to take the children sledging, however. Sara and Sam had to make do playing in the garden. But there were no slopes and it wasn't much fun at all.

4 — Sara and Sam *were* pleased, though, when Mum asked them to go to the corner shop. Then, Mrs Rollins, a neighbour, asked the children if they would fetch groceries, too.

5 — As the children made their way along the snowy pavement, they met Mrs Brown clearing her path. She gave them a shopping list. And so did Mrs Edwards, who lived farther along the street.

6 — In the shop, Sara and Sam handed over the lists. Soon, there was a big pile of shopping. "Oh, dear," sighed Sara. "There's far too much for us to carry."

7 — "But *not* too much for us to *pull*," said Sam, grinning to his sister. "I have an idea, though. Let's hurry back to our garden, and on the way I'll tell you all about it."

8 — Sam and Sara had gone home to fetch their sledge. It was *perfect* for carrying the shopping. "Well done, Sam!" laughed Sara. "We're having fun with our sledge at last!"

Nurse Nancy

Nurse Nancy is the nurse at the Dollies Hospital. Her grandad is the doctor.

1 — It was almost Christmas. Nurse Nancy and Mr Jingle were decorating the hospital tree. "It's nice for the toys who can't go home yet," said Nancy.

4 — "Will you be able to visit the Dollies Hospital?" she asked. "Sorry. I've to visit a hospital in the next town," he replied.

2 — At visiting time, Nancy broke the news to the toys' owners. They were sad that they wouldn't have their toy friends home for Christmas.

3 — Later, Nancy went Christmas shopping. Seeing Father Christmas gave the little nurse an idea.

5 — Back home, Nancy told Grandad. "I can help," smiled Mr Jingle. "Invite everyone to a special Christmas party tomorrow."

6 — So, Father Christmas *was* at the Dollies Hospital! Mr Jingle dressed up. "The toys are having fun after all," chuckled Nancy.

Snowy fun in the park, but . . . Where's

Try to find where these small pictures fit in the main scene.

Patch?

Can you spot the mischievous kitten?

All these words below are hidden in the word square. Can you find them?

S	N	O	W	M	A	N	S
K	C	A	N	S	B	A	E
A	L	C	D	A	N	C	E
T	G	O	D	T	O	H	R
E	C	L	A	U	S	R	T
T	R	E	I	N	D	E	E	R
S	S	E	L	C	I	C	I
K	I	T	T	E	N	I	F

SNOWMAN
FIR
TREES
KITTEN
SNACK
DANCE
HOT DOG
REINDEER
ICICLES
SKATERS
SANTA
CLAUS
ICE

The crooked tree

WINTER had come again to the forest. As the snow fell, the deer looked for shelter under the trees.

A tiny robin lived in a little glade where two small fir trees grew side by side, one small and bushy, the other tall and crooked.

"The children are coming back!" called the robin, one day, as he perched on a branch of the crooked tree. "Remember, they made a promise last year. I wonder if they'll keep it?"

2 — Two little boys and two little girls ran into the clearing. They were dressed warmly against the bitter cold, the pom-poms of their woolly hats bobbing about as they threw snowballs at each other.

"Here is our Christmas tree!" cried the smallest girl, Clara. "Look how tall it has grown!"

"But it's *crooked*!" called her brother, Claus, pointing up at the branches.

"We promised it would be our Christmas tree this year," sighed Gretchen.

"That other tree is better," announced Hans, the oldest boy. "It has nice wide branches to hold our candles."

3 — "Very well," called the other children, "we'll have to take the small tree after all."

The little robin watched sadly as the children began to dig up the bushy fir tree.

When they had finished, they hoisted the tree on to their shoulders and set off home through the snow. Now the crooked fir tree was left alone in the glade with only the little robin to keep him company.

4 — Later, a poor woodman came through the forest. He was the children's father and had been to town to buy presents for his family, but he couldn't afford any of the things he had seen.

"It's Christmas Eve and I have nothing for the children," he sighed. "But they *will* have a Christmas tree."

He soon reached the spot where the two fir trees grew. The woodman stopped and stared at the place where the bushy tree had been.

"No wonder the children took the small tree," he sighed. "This other one is bent and twisted."

5 — Then he clasped the trunk with both hands. "It will do," the man said.

The little robin whispered to the crooked tree, "You are going to be a Christmas tree after all."

The woodman chopped down the crooked tree and dragged it away.

The robin flew after the woodman to his home. There, the man tossed the crooked fir tree beside a pile of logs in his shed.

6 — Then, after supper, the woodman returned to the shed. He chopped off the branches of the fir tree and sawed through the trunk.

All that night, the woodman sat in the shed working. He cut and carved the wood, hammered and painted it.

It was almost dawn when he crept back into the house and tiptoed into the room where his children lay sleeping. Silently, he placed a parcel at the foot of each child's bed.

7 — When the children woke on Christmas morning, the little robin outside heard them cry out with delight as they opened their parcels.

Then, in the afternoon, the robin peeped through the window and saw the woodman light candles on the Christmas tree. He and his children danced round, singing carols.

At last, when Christmas was over, the candles were put away for another year and the bushy little tree was taken outside and chopped up into logs for the fire.

One day, the friendly little robin hopped down to peck at the crumbs the children had left for him on the grass. There, he saw them playing with their new toys.

8 — Claus had a sturdy, painted wooden horse while Hans played with a smart wooden wheelbarrow, which he wheeled over the grass.

Little Clara's father had made her a pretty wooden cradle and Gretchen had been given a lovely doll. The little robin smiled happily to himself.

9 — "The bushy fir tree was beautiful with all its bright coloured candles for only a few short days," he thought. "But now he has gone for ever. When the woodman made these lovely toys from the crooked fir tree, he knew they would keep the children happy *every* day of the year!"

Twinkle

It's Magic

Thread a short piece of string through the sides of a cardboard tube, then knot the ends of the string. Now, covering the string with your hand, ask a friend to drop a ball into the tube. When the string is loose, the ball will fall right through. But, when you pull the string tight, it sticks in the tube, as if by magic!

2	7	6
9	5	1
4	3	8

No matter how you add up these magic numbers, across, down or diagonally, the answer is always 15.

Lay three matchboxes on a table. Pick one up and rattle it to show that it's "full", then shuffle the boxes around and ask your chums to find the "full" one. They never can, because all *three* boxes are empty! The secret is to have a fourth box of spent matches hidden under your sleeve and tied to your wrist with a rubber band. It rattles every time you shake an empty box.

Ask Mum to fix a rubber band across the inside of an old hat with safety pins. When you pull the hat down, then let go — it flies into the air. Your friends will think it's magic hat!

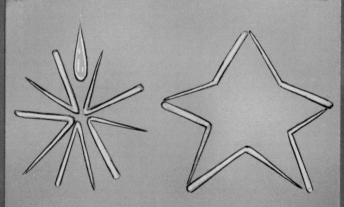

Bend five wooden toothpicks or spent matches, being careful not to break any, and arrange them as shown on the left. Add a drop of water to the centre — then, before your very eyes, you'll see a pointed star appear.

Here's how to get a 10p coin through a hole the size of a 5p piece! Cut a hole the size of a 5p piece in a sheet of paper, then fold the paper in half and place the 10p over the hole. Push the ends of the paper together and watch the 10p drop!

Can you put a hanky underwater without getting it wet? Here's the trick. Pack the hanky into the bottom of a plastic tumbler, then dip the tumbler upside down into a basin of water. Air trapped inside the tumbler stops the water from rising and keeps the hanky dry.

Lower a piece of string into a plastic bottle. Then turn the bottle upside down and give the string a tug. Let the bottle drop and, amazingly, it will swing on the string!

Tell your friends you can lift a sweet out from under a hat without touching the hat. They'll laugh, of course, until you tell them the sweet is gone. When they lift the hat to look, you take the sweet — and you haven't touched the hat!

The trick is to push a ball of modelling clay, just big enough to squeeze through the neck, into the bottle before your friends arrive. When you turn the bottle upside down, the ball traps the string.

Before you begin this trick, lightly stick a coin to the underside of a table with tacky gum. Call your friends, and lay 4 coins on the table top. Say some magic words, then sweep the coins into your hand, carefully pulling loose the hidden coin at the same time. Hold up your hand and — Hey, Presto! — you've turned 4 coins into 5!

The dragon's new toothbrush

WHEN Sophie, the dragon, went to the dentist with her mummy, he told Sophie to clean her teeth or her teeth would go rotten.

Sophie didn't want rotten teeth, but her toothbrush didn't seem to reach them all!

2 — "I'll find a bigger toothbrush!" she decided.

As she set off, Sophie spotted a road sweeper.

"May I buy this broom to clean my teeth?" she asked.

But the road sweeper rushed off in fright.

The next person Sophie saw was a chimney sweep.

"Excuse me," Sophie sighed, and a little flick of flame licked the pavement. "May I buy one of your brushes to clean my teeth?"

The sweep was alarmed.

"Oh, dear me, no," he gulped.

And *he* scurried off, too.

Then a door-to-door salesman caught Sophie's eye. He had an open suitcase — filled with *brushes!*

Sophie smiled her "polite" smile, the one where she did not show all her sharp teeth or breathe fire.

The salesman took one look at Sophie, howled with fright, then ran off.

3 — Farther on, Sophie spotted a little girl hard at work.

"It's not fair!" sighed the girl. "My dad says I've to clear all the weeds from this path. It will take me all day!"

Sophie took a deep breath (an extra-hot one), and blew all over the path.

Hot flames licked the ground and burned out all the weeds in a flash.

"*Yippee!* You've *done* it!" cried the girl, whose name was Jenny. "You've got rid of all the weeds! How can I ever thank you?"

4 — Just then, however, Sophie spotted Jenny's dad washing the car with his new hose-powered water brush.

"That's it!" cried Sophie.

Jenny spoke to her dad and, when he saw how Sophie had burned away all the weeds from the path, he was only too happy to let the dragon try his car brush to clean her teeth.

Sophie ran the brush over her teeth until they sparkled and gleamed.

"This is great," she beamed, giving Jenny her very best and brightest-ever smile. "I'll ask Mum to buy me one!"

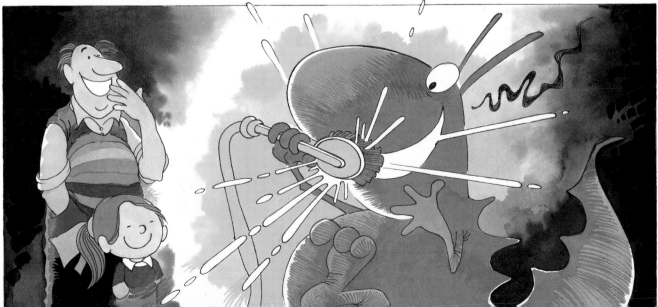

Poppy
Red

TOYS

SPEEDY TREATS

Chocolate Truffles are so easy to make and they taste yummy, too!

YOU WILL NEED
55g cream cheese
55g icing sugar
55g chopped nuts
30g cocoa powder

TO COAT TRUFFLES
Cocoa powder
Desiccated coconut
Chocolate vermicelli

Now get busy!

1 Put the cheese, nuts, icing sugar and cocoa powder into a bowl. Mix together well with a wooden spoon. Roll the mixture into small balls.

2 Put some coconut, chocolate vermicelli and cocoa powder on to three separate plates.

3 Roll each truffle in either the cocoa powder, coconut or vermicelli to coat them. Put the truffles into paper sweet cases.

★ Your tasty truffles are ready to eat, or you could pack them into a pretty box as a gift for your family or friends.

Patch

1 — Paula Perkins has a cute kitten called Patch. He likes to join in whatever Paula does. One day, Paula decided to draw Patch, so she fetched pens and paper and sat the kitten on a cushion. "Now sit still or you'll spoil the drawing," she smiled. "I won't be long."

2 — But Patch was soon bored. That was no fun — he wanted to play instead!

3 — "If you won't sit still for me, then Teddy will," Paula sighed, and she began sketching her favourite toy.